Martyn Plumer's

GREATEST HITS

Martyn Turner's

GREATEST HITS

GILL & MACMILLAN

Gill & Macmillan Ltd
Hume Avenue, Park West, Dublin 12
with associated companies throughout the world
www.gillmacmillan.ie
© Martyn Turner 2003, 2004
First published in paperback 2004
0 7171 3808 9

Design and print origination by O'K Graphic Design, Dublin
Printed in Malaysia

1 3 5 4 2

Also by Martyn Turner

The Book (political cartoons 1973–83), Irish Times Books, Dublin, 1983.
Illuminations – 101 Drawings From Early Irish History, Boethius Press, Kilkenny, 1986.
A Fistful of Dáilers (political cartoons 1983–87), Gill and Macmillan, Dublin 1987.
Not Viking Likely, Irish Life Viking Adventure, Dublin, 1988.
Heavy Weather, Gill and Macmillan, Dublin, 1989.
The Guy Who Won The Tour De France (political cartoons 1987–91), Gill and Macmillan, Dublin, 1991.
The Long Goodbye (a cartoon history of the career of Charles J. Haughey), Irish Times Books, Dublin, 1992.
Politics Et Al (political cartoons 1991–92), Irish Times Books, Dublin, 1992.
The Odd Couple (political cartoons 1992–94), Irish Times Books, Dublin, 1994.
Pack Up Your Troubles: 25 Years of Northern Ireland Cartoons, Blackstaff Press, Belfast, 1995.
The Noble Art of Politics (political cartoons 1994–96), Blackstaff Press, Belfast, 1996.
Brace Yourself, Bridge It (political cartoons 1996–98), Blackstaff Press, Belfast, 1998.
The Golfer's Guide to World History, Blackstaff Press, Belfast, 1999.
Railings (political cartoons 1998–2000), Blackstaff Press, Belfast, 2000.

Edited by Martyn Turner

Thin Black Lines (political cartoons and development education), co-edited with Dr Colm Regan and Scott Sinclair, Development Education Centre, Birmingham, 1988.
Columba! A Cartoon History of South America, co-edited with Dr Colm Regan, Potatoe Press, Dublin, 1993.
Thin Black Lines Rides Again (political cartoons and development education), co-edited with Dr Colm Regan and Scott Sinclair, Development Education Centre, Birmingham, 1994.

Contents

Introduction

Martyn Turner's Greatest Hits was a working title that never got superseded by anything better. My own efforts at naming the 14 or so books I have produced over the last 30 odd years were usually puns based on other people's efforts; *A Fistful of Dáilers* (which came back from the Hong Kong printers in packets marked 'A Fishful of Dollars'), *The Long Goodbye*, *Pack Up Your Troubles*, *The Odd Couple*. I confess that every time I had to think of a title for a collection of political cartoons I was intimidated by the knowledge that Jack Ohman, a cartoonist who operates out of Oregon or thereabouts, had already produced the perfect title for any bunch of political cartoons; 'Do I Have To Draw You A Picture?' Follow that. But this time we have gone for doing exactly what it says on the tin. Except, of course, the 300 or so cartoons herein weren't all hits but then who knows what worked and what didn't. I certainly don't.

Thus the criteria for this selection is pretty much based on what has lasted through the decades rather than what worked at the time. In a Christmas quiz in the *Irish Times* one year they reprinted a cartoon and wrote underneath, 'This cartoon appeared on the front page of the *Irish Times* in February. What news story was it about?' It was one of the questions in that quiz *I* couldn't answer and yet, clearly, at the time I drew it the *Irish Times* had felt it so pertinent and appropriate that they had printed it on the front page. You won't see it reprinted here — or any others that lost their purpose quicker than a Fianna Fáil election manifesto after polling day.

On the odd occasion I meet what George Bush calls folks and everyone else calls people, I usually get complimented on a recent cartoon (usually one drawn by someone else. I used to explain in detail that I didn't do it and was always told I was wrong so, these days, I just say thank you and take full credit) and then get told that the one they really liked was … 'internment for 14 year-old girls', the Yeltsin bottle, the guy who won the Tour de France, the Patriot … The genuine hits. All four of them. The few that struck a chord right across the board.

The rest are ones I like, ones other people have mentioned, ones that got reprinted widely and ones that have survived 30 years and still, sort of, make sense. I have drawn over 9,000 cartoons in the last three decades. *The Phoenix*, that bastion of right-wing nationalist orthodoxy, tells us that they are all the same, which I actually take, in my dotage, as a great compliment. One of my constant companions on the stereo since the late 1960s has been Neil Young. At a concert he replied to someone shouting names of his songs out from the audience with the line, 'Don't worry, they are all the same song.' Well, as bigoted as any northern politician, my views haven't really changed since my teenage years. Set in stone. These are all the same cartoon; only the people, subject, captions and drawing change. The banging my head against the brick wall of right-wing, nationalistic, narrow-minded politics remains the same. Well if it's good enough for Mr Young…

Martyn Turner

P.S. I would like to thank the following people who over the years haven't interfered and have let me get on with what I want to do, drawing it in the way I wanted to draw it and saying what I want to say: Jean Turner (of course), various editors and deputy editors, production helpmates and comment page editors of the *Irish Times* (especially just retired Pat), and a few editors from across the water who contribute to my pension fund from time to time. Thank you. Without people like you, what is left of press freedom in this neck of the woods would be even thinner on the ground than it is.

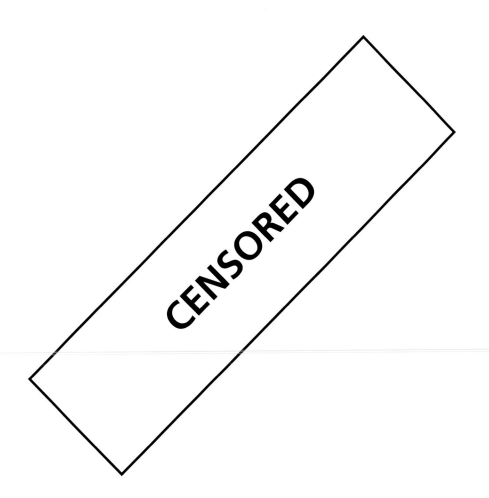

Not wanted...

Here's a few cartoons that didn't get published where they were supposed to be published but, as one man's poison is another man's meat, got befriended by some publication somewhere.

The drawing of Brian Faulkner making a gesture to the minority was rejected by the (now defunct) *Sunday News* in Belfast on grounds of poor taste. It was published by the *Irish Times*.

But it was poor taste that kept the cartoon about Pat Buchanan out of the *Irish Times*. A night editor (now defunct) decreed that *Irish Times* readers didn't want to see 'elephant shit at their breakfast table' and replaced it with a cartoon on the same subject that I had rejected myself. Gloriously, I flogged it to an English Sunday paper for a three-figure sum. They, of course, being English, have no taste at all.

Bishop Casey. Ah, Bishop Casey. The *Irish Times* told me, in a rare display of editorial interference (they are the least interfering of any of the newspapers I have crossed swords with over the years), that it would have to be a very good cartoon indeed for me to get any comment about Bishop Casey into the paper. It was a sensitive subject. I sent them the enclosed and they went into conclave for two days before rejecting it. It became the cover of *Fortnight*.

When Charles J. Haughey announced his imminent retirement, the *Irish Times* decided on a special supplement where they reprinted a few articles and some of my old cartoons and also asked me to do a new one, in colour. I submitted the '35 years of public service…' and it didn't get printed.

'Why?' I asked.

'Because the lawyers said it was libellous.'

'But it's true.'

'That doesn't matter,' they said, 'and even though it is true it would be up to us to prove, in court, the implication that he was living beyond his means.'

Now, of course, it has been proved by McCracken and the

Revenue Commissioners. But it shows the straightjacket that the press in Ireland operates under. How many of the tribunals we have now would have been necessary if we had a truly free press? A cartoon in this book somewhere is a caricature of Ray Burke, an auctioneer, standing by a 'For Sale' sign. When I drew it, the double entendre hadn't actually occurred to me, but it occurred to the legal eagles of the *Irish Times* and I had to change it. Ray Burke, at the time, hadn't been tribunalised. We didn't know, officially, that he was as much for sale as any of his properties. What, as they say, the dogs in the street knew, wasn't allowed to be known in the public print. We get the country we deserve. We voted in these politicians who legislate their restrictive and self-serving laws. Here endeth the lesson.

Vikings hurt the old, the sick, and the handicapped.

Manager darts in and removes a Turner

By Renagh Holohan

A POSTER by the political cartoonist Martyn Turner, commissioned for the Art on the DART project, was pasted over on the order of a senior manager in Iarnrod Eireann immediately after the exhibition was opened at Pearse Station, Westland Row, Dublin, yesterday morning.

The 20-foot by 10-foot exhibit entitled ''Election poster 988 AD'' shows the Taoiseach, Mr Haughey, and the Minister for Finance, Mr MacSharry, dressed as Vikings and carried the caption ''Vikings hurt the old, the sick and the handicapped''. It was one of eight posters and six exhibits produced by various artists to mark the Dublin Millennium. The remaining seven posters are still on view at Pearse Station and the exhibits can be seen on DART trains.

LET'S be clear. There can be no justification for the withdrawal of a Martyn Turner poster from the Art on the DART exhibition at Pearse Station, Westland Row. To start even considering a justification is to speak the language of the censor. Art, like literature or journalism, has no value unless it is freely expressed. Having a democratic society means living with the consequences of free expression no matter how uncomfortable.

One would hope that other artists will show solidarity with Turner, as happened some years ago when a Robert Ballagh kite was suppressed by the Kilkenny Arts Week.

VIKING CUTS

Sir,—Regarding Martyn Turner's cartoon (November 3rd) commissioned by the clever DART Art Millennium poster display, may I comment that the greatest insult perceived or imagined was to compare the present Fianna Fail leadership to the Vikings. The Vikings were only in the ha'penny place. — Yours, etc.,

MARY McEVOY
Quinn's Road,
Shankhill,
Co. Dublin.

* * *

Sir,—The removal by Iarnród Eireann of the Haughey-MacSharry cartoon from Pearse Station is to be applauded, for such a cartoon is deeply insulting and grossly offensive to Vikings. — Yours, etc.,

DERMOT P. CURRAN,
176 Sycamores,
Kilkenny.

'FF jibe' ban derails art

By JEROME REILLY

THE CENSORSHIP of a satirical cartoon featuring the Taoiseach Mr. Haughey and Finance Minister Ray MacSharry has led to a major row between Irish Rail and a number of the country's best known artists. The billboard-sized cartoon, from the nib of Martyn Turner, was blanked out last week by Irish Rail within hours of it being exhibited at Pearse Station as part of the ''Art on the DART'' scheme.

The cartoon itself depicts an axe-wielding Mr. Haughey with Minister MacSharry in Viking garb complete with helmets. The caption says: ''Vikings hurt the old, sick and handicapped.''

Irish Rail said it was their policy not to permit materials of a political

Now seven other artists have decided to withdraw their work which is also on display, in protest at the ''blatant'' censorship of Martyn Turner's work.

nature to be displayed in their stations or on their premises.

Yesterday the Douglas Hyde Gallery said that, in protest at the move, they had requeted Irish Rail to remove the remaining works from the billboard project.

And last night an Irish Rail spokesman said they would agree to the Gallery's request to have the remaining works pasted over but with much regret.

P.S. The other cartoon was done for 'Art on the DART', one of a series of art posters commissioned for display at railway stations. CIE decided they didn't want to deride their political masters and covered it up. The other artists who had been commissioned withdrew their works in solidarity. Thus, instead of just being seen by commuters from the south side, it made the front page of the *Irish Times* instead. Sometimes banning things is more of a hassle than letting them be.

Governments
of the People

Liam Cosgrave 1973–77

When I moved down from Belfast in 1976 to increase my contributions to the *Irish Times*, the Fine Gael/Labour coalition was coming to the end of its term. But it was there long enough for me to realise how difficult my new job was going to be. How, for example, can one satirise a Taoiseach who votes against his own government's bill, as Liam Cosgrave did? Apart from being opposed to contraception (that was the bill), he was also hot on law and order and had a dislike of 'mongrel foxes'. One of his ministers called the then President a 'thundering disgrace' which led to the limerick printed hereabouts. When I delivered that cartoon, by hand in those days, an editor looked at it and said, 'this is libellous' and, turning to a sub editor added, 'put it on the front page'.

Richie Ryan

Some lines on the occasion of a
Ministerial speech at Mullingar

While addressing the troops bold and handsome,
His pre-arranged speech overran some,
The T.D. from Louth,
Put his foot in his mouth
And spoke out the back of his transom.

Paddy Donegan

Jack Lynch 1977–79

Jack Lynch's third term of office became the battle-ground for post-Arms-Trial Fianna Fáil. George Colley was Minister for Finance. It was, as they say, a pivotal moment in Irish politics as the shenanigans of Fianna Fáil at this time are still dominating much of our politics today. Who would have thought.

GREAT LEADERS OF OUR TIME. No. 36

The **AYALOTTA YOURMONEY**

Spiritual opponent of
thousands of PAYE sect taxpayers.

George Colley

Charles Haughey 1979–81, February–November 1982, 1987–92

As a taste of things to come there was a minor scandal in CJH's first go at being Supreme Leader when bugs were discovered in the Dáil telephone system. As usual the real culprit was the press who chose to mention it.

In 1982 Fianna Fáil returned to office when the first FitzGerald government collapsed over putting VAT on children's shoes. Surviving with the aid of independent votes, Mr Haughey attempted to rekindle his political love affair with Margaret Thatcher and attempted to quell the backbench discontent that eventually led to the formation of the Progressive Democrats in December 1985.

His third whack at it included a spell governing on Fianna Fáil's own and a spell in conjunction with the PDs, breaking the lifelong FF core value of never going into coalition. It was during this spell that Charlie knocked Stephen Roche off the winner's podium at the Tour de France, visited Belfast, lived beyond his means and, eventually, was dragged from office by the PDs whilst claiming that he would be 'going with dignity'.

Further Fianna Fáil scandals involving telephones also took place under his watch. Journalists' phones were bugged and the Fianna Fáil candidate for the Presidency, Brian Lenihan, was politically damaged because of a phone call he made and a tape-recorded interview he gave. FF and technology just don't go together.

ONE LUMP OR TWO?

OUCH!

1983. THE RESUMPTION OF THE SPECIAL RELATIONSHIP AFTER FIANNA FAIL ELECTION VICTORY

Taoiseach says he will 'go with dignity'

Garret FitzGerald 1981–82, 1982–87

Despite inheriting a pretty awful economic situation after some Fianna Fáil giveaway electioneering, the two governments of Garret FitzGerald became embroiled in constitutional matters. The interminable wrangling over abortion and divorce became the main feature of the time, which went on and on and on and on. We should be due another referendum sometime soon, shouldn't we? The period also saw the creation of the Progressive Democrats. The coalition with Labour limped on until the general election of 1987 when Fine Gael lost 20 seats and dropped 12 percentage points in the poll.

It was revealed that King George's demise was arranged to time with the headlines of the **Morning** papers.

Albert Reynolds 1992–94

Albert Reynolds, against whom I would not say a word as he tends to sue, brought a whole new business dynamism to politics. Unfortunately this didn't rest easy with coalition partners and he fell out with the PDs and, eventually, with their replacement, Dick Spring's Labour Party. But he tried to rid FF of Haugheyism, an impossible task, as well as splitting more abortion hairs, playing the poor mouth successfully in Europe, and getting the first hint of the clerical sexual abuse scandals that dominated the headlines latterly. His plan to greet President Yeltsin on the tarmac at Shannon did not go well. There were a few hiccups.

John Bruton 1994–97

Taking over when Labour jumped the Fianna Fáil ship, John Bruton introduced transparency into government. His Minister for Agriculture improved on this by introducing bi-location into government by claiming to be in two places at the same time. John Bruton's alleged best friend, Michael Lowry, was caught doing something or other, alleged. Just went to show that Fine Gael were well able to replace Fianna Fáil: given the chance they could be just as dodgy.

Bertie Ahern 1997
– still limping along

There are a lot more cartoons in this section for many reasons. One is that events are so recent that they don't need explanation, I hope. The other is that, with the instigation of the tribunals, the rottenness in the state of Ireland that took place in the last 30 years is now coming into the full light of day.

Padraig Flynn

The Environment

Here are a few cartoons that loosely come under the heading 'environmental'. They are mostly self-explanatory except, perhaps, for younger readers, those concerning Carnsore Point. It may be hard to believe that the political parties who so actively object to Sellafield these days actively intended Ireland to have its very own nuclear power plant back in the early 70s. Carnsore Point. Those of us who objected at the time were given the usual abuse. The Chernobyl and Three Mile Island disasters changed minds that our arguments had not.

PROPOSAL: SITE FOR NUCLEAR PLANT THAT WILL CONVINCE US THAT SUCH THINGS CAN BE CLEAN AND SAFE.

The North

This is one section that needs no explanatory text since the same things happen over and over again, ad nauseam, in the North. Even the main actors don't seem to change too much. These are probably all the same cartoon. As I write this in April, whilst George W. Bush is in Hillsborough, we are told this is the most momentous week in the North's politics since the last momentous week. Hopefully, as this book is produced these cartoons can be consigned to history, and the peace process can become just…peace.

KING BULLY

THE NORTHERN
PARAMILITARIES
ENGAGE IN THE
PAINFUL PROCESS OF
DECOMMISSIONING ARMS...

...AND LEGS... AND ELBOWS... AND KNEES...AND HEADS....

TRADITIONAL ROUTE

CATHOLIC COMMUNITY

The HAND of HISTORY

The CLAWS of HISTORY

New World Order in slightly random order

Hands up those
who would believe
a report that
says there is little
evidence that
Chernobyl has
damaged health...

Imelda and Ferdinand Marcos

Gorbachev

Gaddafi

BEWARE OF THE DOG

THE HOUND OF THE BASQUE-VILLES   Franco

Mao

Castro

March 1991.

The freedom of Kuwait, the return of the Government and the restoration of one man, one vote.......

.....and this is the man who has that one vote..

JUST A YEAR AFTER INCREDIBLE VICTORY IN THE GULF WAR IT'S BACK ON THE OLD CAMPAIGN TRAIL, FULL TIME......

....(FOR GEORGE BUSH, TOO)......

CAMPAIGN TO DEFY THE U.N.

CAMPAIGN AGAINST SHIAS AND KURDS

CAMPAIGN FOR NUCLEAR CAPABILITY

The mother of all battles

The mother of all defeats

The mother of all victory parades

The children......

And then there was the War . . .

THE LEADERS of THE FREE WORLD ARE TERRIFIED THAT **IRAQ** HAS DEVICES THAT COULD DESTROY WESTERN CIVILISATION......

...THEY ARE CALLED VALVES...